BEST OF BEYONCÉ

FOR PIANO, VOICE & G

WISE PUBLICATIONS

part of The Music Sales Group

London / New York / Paris / Sydney / Copenhagen / Berlin / Madrid / Hong Kong / Tokyo

Published by
Wise Publications
14-15 Berners Street, London W1T 3LJ, UK.

Exclusive Distributors:
Music Sales Limited
Distribution Centre, Newmarket Road,
Bury St Edmunds, Suffolk IP33 3YB, UK.

Music Sales Pty Limited
20 Resolution Drive,
Caringbah, NSW 2229, Australia.

Order No. AM1004795
ISBN: 978-1-78038-574-7
This book © Copyright 2012 by Wise Publications.

Edited by Jenni Norey.
Cover designed by Lizzie Barrand.
Photographs: pages 2 & 4 © LFI; page 5 © Getty Images.

Printed in the the EU.

Your Guarantee of Quality
As publishers, we strive to produce every book
to the highest commercial standards.
The music has been freshly engraved and the
book has been carefully designed to minimise
awkward page turns and to make playing from
it a real pleasure.
Particular care has been given to specifying acid-free,
neutral-sized paper made from pulps which have not
been elemental chlorine bleached.
This pulp is from farmed sustainable forests and was
produced with special regard for the environment.
Throughout, the printing and binding have been
planned to ensure a sturdy, attractive publication
which should give years of enjoyment.
If your copy fails to meet our high standards,
please inform us and we will gladly replace it.

www.musicsales.com

When Destiny's Child first emerged from Houston, Texas, in 1997, few would have predicted that Beyoncé Knowles, their 16-year-old leader, would become a household name less than a decade later. The group, supported by a myriad of producers, made snappy urban music, with lyrics often based on overheard conversations from the hair salon owned by Beyoncé's mother, Tina.

The departure of three members in quick succession at the turn of the 21st century gave Destiny's Child notoriety, which they successfully turned into commerciality with three self-mythologising singles, 'Independent Women Part I', 'Survivor' and 'Bootylicious'.

Beyoncé soon left the group behind and has become a phenomenon, with mass appeal. Although part of a direct line from the classic soul divas of the Sixties and Seventies, her appeal seems wider and more mainstream. Beyoncé's love and understanding of music is indisputable, as is her talent and her ability to maximise opportunities and work across a variety of platforms – music, film, television, fashion and, recently, perfume. By the end of the 00s, she had won 16 Grammy Awards and had flashmobs around the world dancing to her 'Single Ladies (Put A Ring On It)'.

BEAUTIFUL LIAR

Words & Music by Mikkel Eriksen, Beyonce Knowles,
Tor Erik Hermansen, Amanda Ghost & Ian Dench

for a beau - ti - ful liar. Oh! Can't__ we laugh__ a - bout it?

Oh! It's__ not worth__ our time. Oh! We__ can live__ with-out him;

1. just a beau - ti - ful liar.

2. just a beau - ti - ful liar.

2. I

BEST THING I NEVER HAD

Words & Music by Kenneth Edmonds, Antonio Dixon, Patrick Smith,
Beyoncé Knowles, Larry Griffin, Caleb McCampbell & Robert Taylor

15

place,___ an - oth - er time, an - oth - er world,___ an - oth - er life. Thank

God I found the good in good - bye.___ I used to want you so bad.___

D.S. al Coda

Coda

Best thing you nev - er had.___ I used to want you so bad.___

I'm so through with that.___ 'Cause hon - est - ly you___

17

Goes a - round, comes back a - round.

(Goes a - round, comes back a - round.)

Bet it sucks to be you right now.

(Goes a - round comes back a - round.)

Bet it sucks to be you right now.

(Goes a - round comes back a - round.)

Bet it sucks to be you right now.

BROKEN-HEARTED GIRL

Words & Music by Kenneth "Babyface" Edmonds, Mikkel S. Eriksen,
Tor Erik Hermansen & Beyoncé Knowles

1. You're ev-'ry-thing I thought you nev-er were____ and noth-ing like I thought you could__ have been..
2. There's some-thing that I feel I need__ to say,____ but up till now I've al-ways been__ a-fraid

____ But still, you live in-side____ of me, so tell me how is that?
____ that you would nev-er come____ a-round, but still I want to put this out.

Dm   C

know I'll be there at the end of the day.
I will be there   at the end of the day.

Dm   B♭

I don't wan-na be with-out you, babe,   I don't want a bro-ken heart. Don't

F   C/E

wan-na take a breath with-out you, babe.   I don't want to play that part.   I

Dm   B♭   F

know that I love you, but let me just say,   I don't wan-na love you in

no kind - a way. No,_ no,___ I don't wan-na bro-ken heart,_ And I don't wan-na play the bro - ken-heart - ed girl._

1.

_ No,___ no,___ no bro-ken-heart-ed girl.

I'm no bro-ken-heart-ed girl._____

no bro-ken-heart-ed girl._____ Now I'm at a place I thought_ I'd nev-er be._____ Ooh._____

I'm liv-in' in a world that's all___ a-bout you and me,_____ yeah.

Ain't got-ta be af-raid, my bro - ken heart_ is free, to spread_ my___ wings and fly___ a - way,___

___ a - way___ with-a you.___

CRAZY IN LOVE

Words & Music by Beyonce Knowles, Shawn Carter & Rich Harrison

Uh oh uh oh uh oh, oh no no. *History in the making.* *Part two. So crazy right now.*

1. I look and stare so deep in your eyes. I touch on you more and more ev-'ry time.
2. When I talk to my friends so qui-et-ly. *(Who he thinks he is?)* Look at what you did to me.

When you leave I'm beg-ging you not to go. Call your name two or three times in a row.
Ten-nis shoes, don't e-ven need to buy a new dress. If you ain't there, ain't no-bod-y else to im-press.

Such a fun-ny thing for me to try to ex-plain, how I'm feel-in' and my pride is the one to blame.
It's the way that you know what I thought I knew. It's the beat that my heart skips when I'm with you.

Look-ing so cra-zy your love's_ got me look-ing, got me look-ing so cra-zy your love._

1.

Uh oh uh oh uh oh, oh no no. Uh oh uh oh uh oh, oh no no.

Uh oh uh oh uh oh, oh no no. Uh oh uh oh uh oh, oh no no.

2.

Look-ing so cra-zy your love's_ got me look-ing, got me look-ing so cra-zy your love._

1.
B♭ ... G

Star like Rin - go, roll like green Cor - vette. Cra - zy, bring your whole set.

2.
B♭ ... G

Got me look - ing_____ so cra - zy, my ba - by I'm

B♭ ... G

not my - self____ late - ly. I'm fool - ish, I don't do this. I've been

B♭ ... G⁷

play - ing my - self____ ba - by, I don't_ care._____ 'Cause your_ love's_

2°Rap:
Jay Z in the range, crazy and deranged,
They can't figure him out they like, hey is he insane?
Yes sir, I'm cut from a different cloth,
My texture is the best fur, of chinchilla.
Been dealing with chain smokers,
But how you think I got the name Hova?
I been realer the game's over,
Fall back young.
Ever since the label changed over
To platinum the game's been a wrap, one.

DÉJÀ VU

Words & Music by Rodney Jerkins, Shawn Carter, Makeba Riddick,
Beyoncé Knowles, Kellie Nicole Price, Delisha Thomas & John Webb

Gm⁹

get o - ver you. 'Cause ev -'ry - thing___ I see is you. And I don't want___

no sub - sti - tute. Ba - by I swear___ it's Dé - jà Vu. Know that I can't___

get o - ver you. 'Cause ev -'ry - thing___ I see is you. And I don't want___

1.

To Coda ⊕

no sub - sti - tute. Ba - by I swear___ it's Dé - jà

2.

___ it's Dé - jà

four - fours. Like I'm from the H. O. U. S. T. O. N.

Blow wind, so Chi-ca-go of him. Is he the best ev - er, that's the ar - gu - a - ment.

I don't make the list, don't be mad at me.__ I just make the hits like a fac - tor three.__ I'm

just one to one noth-in' af - ter me.__ No Dé - jà Vu, just me and my oh!

Ba - by, I can't__

it's Dé - jà Vu. Know that I can't___ get o - ver you. 'Cause ev -'ry - thing___

___ I see is you. And I don't want___ no sub - sti - tute. Ba - by I swear___

A♭maj⁹   Gmaj⁹

___ it's Dé - jà Vu.

A♭maj⁹   Gmaj⁹

N.C.

HALO

Words & Music by Ryan Tedder, Beyoncé Knowles & Evan Bogart

45

IF I WERE A BOY

Words & Music by Tobias Gad & Britney Carlson

*Recorded a half step lower.

IRREPLACEABLE

Words & Music by Mikkel Eriksen, Beyonce Knowles, Espen Lind,
Amund Bjorklund, Tor Erik Hermansen & Shaffer Smith

must not know 'bout me.___ I could have an-oth-er you__ by to-mor-row so don't you

ev-er for a se-cond get to think - ing. You must not know 'bout me,___ you

-oth-er you__ for to-mor-row, don't you ev-er for a se-cond get to think-

-ing you're ir - re-place-a - ble.___

ME, MYSELF AND I

Words & Music by Scott Storch, Robert Waller & Beyoncé Knowles

now on I'm gon' be my own best friend. Got me my-self___ and I.___ My eyes have

(Vocal ad lib.)

cried a thou - sand times.___ I can't re - gret time spent___ with you.__

___ S'how I learned how to make___ it through.___ Now I've got

Vocal ad lib.

SINGLE LADIES

Words & Music by Beyonce Knowles, Christopher Stewart,
Terius Nash & Thaddis Harrell

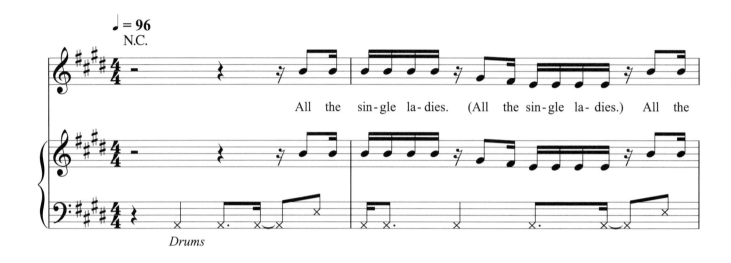

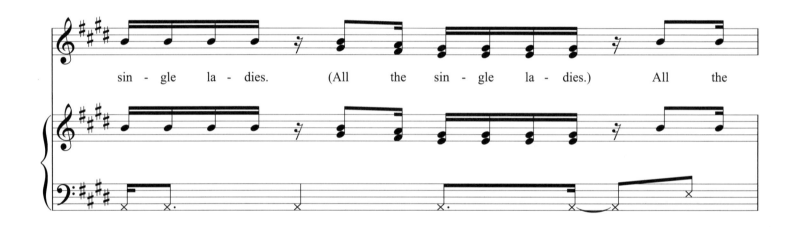

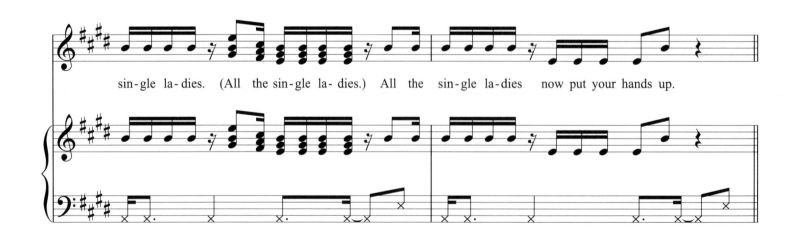

love is what I pre-fer, what I de-serve.___ Here's a man that makes_ me then takes_ me and de-

-li-vers me to a des-ti-ny,_ to in-fi-ni-ty and be-yond. Pull me in - to your arms say

I'm the one you want._ If you don't you'll be a-lone_ and like a ghost, I'll be gone._ All the

Drums

sin-gle la-dies. (All the sin-gle la- dies.) All the sin-gle la- dies. (All the sin-gle la- dies.) All the

SWEET DREAMS

Words & Music by Richard Butler, Wayne Wilkins, James Scheffer
& Beyoncé Knowles

(Turn the lights on.)

1. Ev-'ry night I rush to my bed___ with hopes that may-be I'll get a chance___ to see you when I close my

eyes. I'm go-ing out of my head,___ lost in a fai-ry-tale, can you hold my hands_ and be my

guide?_ Clouds filled with stars cov-er your skies and I hope it rains._

You're the per - fect lul - la - by._____ What kind-a dream is this?_ You could be a

sweet dream or a beau - ti - ful night - mare._ Eith-er way I___

don't wan-na wake up from you. Sweet dream or a beau - ti - ful night - mare._

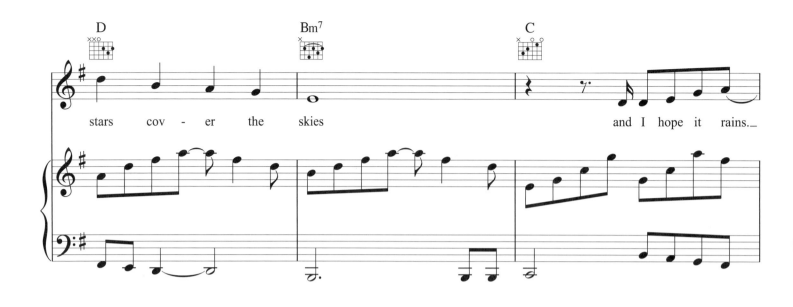

stars cov - er the skies and I hope it rains.

D.S. al Coda

You're the per - fect lul - la - by.

Coda

don't wan - na wake up from you. Tat - too your

81

LISTEN

Words & Music by Henry Krieger, Anne Preven, Scott Cutler
& Beyoncé Knowles

you,___ you don't know what I'm feel-ing I'm more than what,___ you've made of me,___ I

fol-lowed the voice_ you think you gave to me,___ but now I've got-ta find___

my own,_____ my own.

123456789